Santa's Busy Day

Sticker & Activity Fun

igloobooks

Santa's Late Morning

It's the morning of Christmas Eve and Santa's alarm clock hasn't gone off!
Can you help Santa quickly find his Christmas outfit?

coat

boots

hat

belt

Answers on page 16

Flying-Feed Recipe

Santa's elves need help remembering the recipe for the reindeer's special, flying feed. Each pair of ingredients must add up to seven.

6 Carrot Tops

18 Figs

4 Secret ingredient

14 Seaweed

1 Corn

13 Frogs' Legs

8 Pumpkin seeds

5 Elf dust

7 Newts' eyes

11 Chocolate

2 Oats

3 Dried fruit

Ingredient		Ingredient	
	+		= 7
	+		= 7
	+		= 7

Answers on page 16

Reindeer Training

Help Santa pair up his reindeer ready for training.
The pairs are wearing matching outfits.

Mylo's First Day

Mylo the elf is starting his first day at Santa's Christmas village.
Help Mylo find his way to the toy factory so he can report for duty.

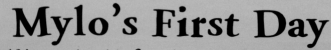

Start →

TOY FACTORY

Answers on page 16

A Musical Mix-up

Mylo has mixed up his toy files. Follow the clues below and write a "G" on the file if the child is getting a guitar, or "D" if the child is getting a drum set.

CLUES

- Gary is getting a guitar. He has brown hair, a green top and wears glasses.
- Holly is getting a guitar. She has brown hair, is wearing a headband and has a red top.
- Steve is getting drums. He has blond hair and is wearing a red jumper.
- Melanie is getting drums. She has a green top, brown hair and is wearing a necklace.
- Jason is getting a guitar. He has blond hair, is wearing glasses and has a blue top.
- Rebecca is getting drums. She is wearing glasses and has blonde hair and a green top.
- Matt is getting a guitar. He is smiling, has a green top and brown hair.
- Gabby is getting drums. She has a blue top, wears glasses and has blonde hair.
- Dave is getting drums. He has blond hair and a yellow top.
- Nicky is getting a guitar. She has a blue top, auburn hair and is wearing a hairband.

Answers on page 16

Christmas Gift Wrap

Follow the steps below to make your own festive gift wrap.

You will need:

brown parcel paper

potato

scissors and knife

paper plates

paints

 1

Unroll the parcel paper and ask an adult to cut off the amount you need to wrap your present.

 **2**

Cut a potato in half. On the flat end, draw a star shape and ask an adult to carve around the shape.

 3

Pour your paint on to plates.

 **4**

Dip your star-shaped potato stamp in your paint and press firmly on to the parcel paper.

 5

Once your paint is dry, you can wrap up your present!

Top Tip

Why not try different Christmas shapes, such as a holly leaf, a bell, or even a present.

Present Picking

Santa and his elves are busy sorting all the presents ready for Christmas.
Can you spot seven differences between picture A and picture B?

Answers on page 16

The Christmas Chimney Game

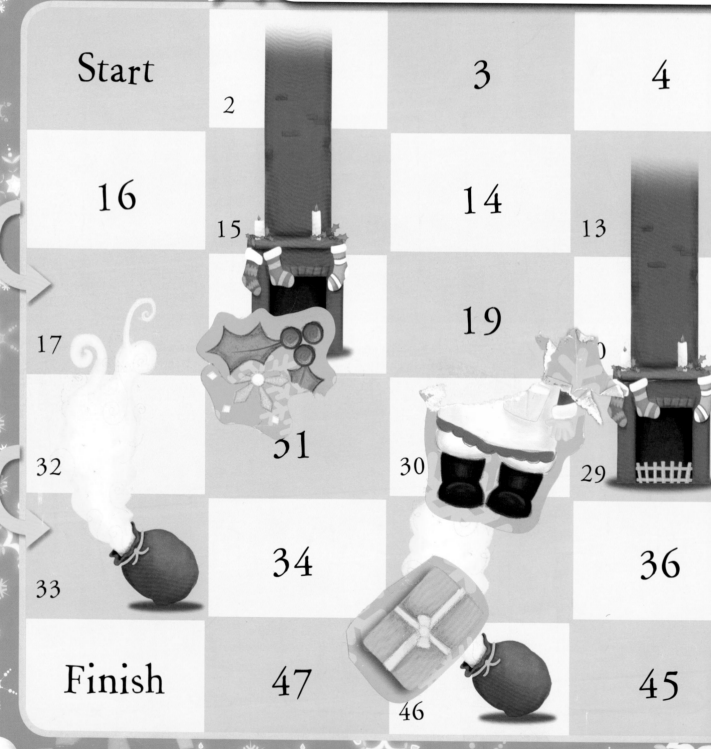

Start

2

3

4

16

14

15

13

17

19

20

32

31

30

29

33

34

36

Finish

47

46

45

Place each players' counter on the start square. Each player takes it in turn to roll the dice and moves their counter the number of squares shown on the dice. If your counter lands on a chimney top, slide down the chimney to the fireplace square below. If your counter lands on a bag of elf dust, float up to the top of the dust cloud. You have to roll the exact number to land on the finish square. First player to the finish wins!

5

6

7

8

12

11

10

9

21

22

23

24

27

26

25

38

39

40

43

42

41

All I Want For Christmas

What do you really want for Christmas? Get your best pens at the ready and draw your perfect Christmas present in the space below.

The Present List

Help Santa memorize the presents and their gift tags. Look at the image for 20 seconds and turn over to answer a quick memory test quiz.

Dotty Gifts

Join the dots below and find out what Santa has got Mrs Santa for Christmas. Once you have completed the picture, use your best pens to decorate it.

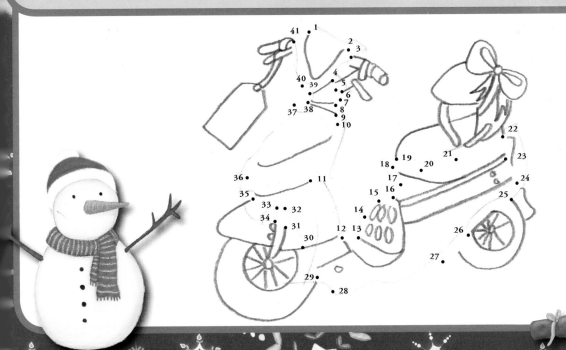

Answers on page 16

The Present List Quiz

You have studied the Present List pictures from page 11, now test your memory and answer the questions below. Remember, no peeking!

1. What is Alice getting for Christmas?

2. Who is getting a boat as a Christmas present?

3. How many presents had bows?

4. How many presents were there in total?

Toy Testing

Santa's elves are busy testing the quality of this year's presents. Help the elves find the right pieces to complete the jigsaw.

A

B

C

D

Answers on page 16

Packing Santa's Sack

It's nearly time for Santa to set off and Santa and his elves are busy packing his sack. Study the picture and answer the questions below.

Answers on page 16

1. How many elves are carrying red presents?

2. How many elves can you spot?

3. How many carrots can you find?

Reindeer Routes

Santa is busy delivering presents. A gust of wind blows his route list out of his hands. Help Santa work out where he needs to deliver the next three presents.

Santa's route

3 6 9 ◯ ◯ ◯

Answers on page 16

Christmas Morning

Santa has been busy all night and now children everywhere are waking up.
Get your best pens and decorate the picture below. Happy Christmas!

Answers

Page 2: Santa's Late Morning

Page 3: Flying-Feed Recipe

Corn + Carrot Tops
Oats + Elf Dust
Dried Fruit + Secret Ingredient

Page 4: Reindeer Training

A and C, B and G, D and E, F and Hz

Mylo's First Day

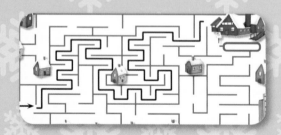

Page 5: A Musical Mix-Up

A=D, B=D, C=G, D=G, E=G, F=D, G=D,
H=D, I=G, J=G

Page 7: Present Picking

Page 11: Dotty Gift

Santa has given Mrs Santa a moped
for Christmas

Page 12: The Present List Quiz

1. Teddy Bear
2. Jack
3. Four presents have bows
4. There are seven presents

Toy Testing: A, C and D

Page 13: Packing Santa's Sack

1. There are six elves carrying red presents
2. There are eighteen elves in total
3. There is one carrot

Page 14: Delivery Route

The next three houses are: No.12, No.15
and No.18

Happy
Christmas!